Grade 7

Roads to Reasoning

Developing Thinking Skills Through Problem Solving

Stephen Krulik and

Jesse A. Rudnick

Acknowledgments

Project Editors
Harriet Slonim, Susan McMahon

Writers
Stephen Krulik, Jesse A. Rudnick

Design Director
Karen Stack

Cover Design and Illustration
Aki Nurosi

Design
Gerta Sorensen

Illustration
Susan Aiello Studio

Composition
Graphic Advantage, Ltd.

Two Prudential Plaza
Chicago, IL 60601

Printed in the United States of America.

ISBN 0-7622-1353-1
Customer Service 800-624-0822
www.creativepublications.com

1 2 3 4 5 6 7 8 VHG 07 06 05 04 03 02

Contents

Introduction

Rationale

MOST MATHEMATICS EDUCATORS AGREE that the development of reasoning power is a primary objective of elementary mathematics. In fact, problem solving, which is the basis for developing reasoning power, has been at the forefront of the mathematics curriculum for many years. The National Council of Teachers of Mathematics' *Principles and Standards,* released in 2000, continues to emphasize both of these areas. Within the thinking and reasoning domain, the area that requires the greatest attention is the development of higher-order thinking skills, specifically critical and creative thinking.

Critical thinking is the ability to analyze a situation and draw appropriate and correct conclusions from the given data.
It also includes determining whether data are inconsistent or if data may be missing or extraneous.

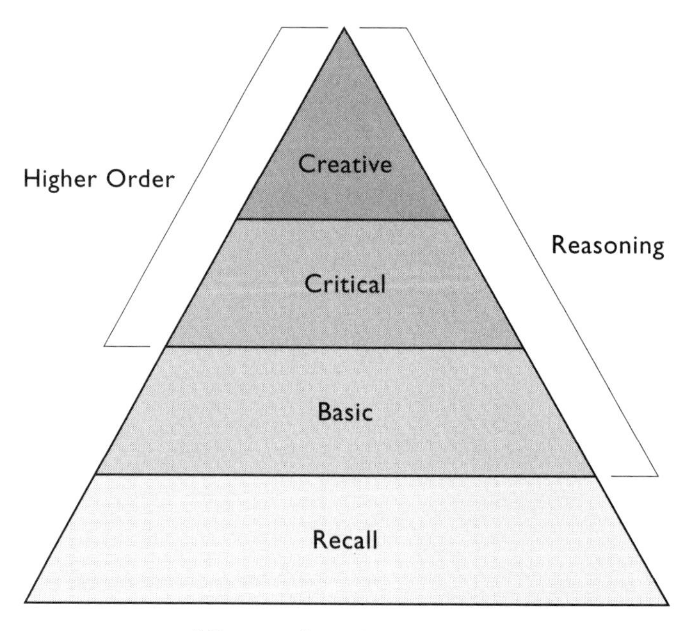

Hierarchy of Thinking

Creative thinking is the ability to originate a solution to a problem situation. In addition, it is the ability to generate, synthesize, and apply original ideas to produce a complex product.

Reasoning is the ultimate goal of the books in this series. Problem solving is the road that will lead to an increased ability to reason. The problems in this book are vehicles that carry the students along the road, and the teacher is the driver who guides the students.

Most mathematics textbook series include some degree of problem solving. This series provides additional practice using a variety of approaches that will further develop reasoning power. As students experience a variety of strategies for solving problems, they will become more flexible in their thinking and reasoning.

There is a strong connection between the problems in this series and the language arts—reading, writing, listening, and speaking. Careful reading of a word problem is often as important as mathematical skills for successfully solving the problem. It is critical that students

1) read the problem carefully,
2) find out what they are being asked to do,
3) solve the problem, and
4) determine whether or not the answer makes sense.

What's in This Book?

This book contains six sections, each of which focuses on a specific aspect of the problem-solving process. The sections also serve to strengthen students' reasoning skills.

Section 1: What Number Makes Sense?

This section contains problems and solutions from which numerical data has been removed. Students choose from a list of numbers to fill in the blanks so that the problems and solutions make sense.

Section 2: What's Wrong?

In this section students are given problems with solutions that contain errors in reasoning. Students identify the errors in reasoning and find the correct solutions to the problems.

Section 3: What Would You Do?

This section features open-ended problem situations. In each case, students solve the problem based upon their experiences, knowledge of the situation, and individual preference, and then support their solutions.

Section 4: What Questions Can You Answer?

This section contains mathematical settings with numerical data. Students generate a list of questions that can be answered based on the data and then answer at least one of their questions.

Section 5: What's Missing?

Each problem in this section is missing data required to solve the problem. Students identify what is missing, supply appropriate data, and then solve the problem.

Section 6: What's the Question if You Know the Answer?

This section contains problem situations that include data but no questions. Students are given several possible answers for which they must supply appropriate questions.

How to Use This Book

Each section begins with a teaching lesson that guides students through a problem similar to the other problems in the section. Suggested questions are provided. Responses generated in discussion during the teaching lesson allow students an opportunity to share their thinking and listen to the thinking of their peers. These discussions help students clarify their understanding of the process for solving the problems in the section.

The teaching lessons are designed to guide students as they are learning procedures. Depending on the needs of your students, you may also want to consider using other problems in a section for whole-group lessons. A great deal of interesting dialogue and thoughtful questioning can occur during these whole-class lessons.

The problems in this book can be used in a variety of ways.

Class Opener or Warm-Up

Present the problem as an opening exercise to involve students in a discussion that can carry over into the day's lesson.

Class Closer

If there are a few minutes left at the end of a class period, introduce a problem in class and assign it as a homework or a family activity. Have students discuss the work at the beginning of the next day.

Small-Group or Partners Activity

After you have introduced a section with the teaching lesson, most students will be able to solve the remaining problems with a partner or in a small group. Working in this way, students can share their thinking with their peers and get important feedback.

Individual Activity

After students have participated in the teaching lesson and worked with a partner or small group, many will be ready to solve additional problems individually. The ability to work these problems independently may vary from student to student.

Assessment

Suggested answers to problems in this book can be found at the end of each section. A rubric is also provided to help you evaluate students' reasoning. You might even decide to check one section, or certain problems within a section, using the answer key and to assess other sections or problems within a section using a rubric.

A rubric is helpful in assessing a student's mathematical proficiency in relationship to specific criteria. A rubric can also help to more reliably assess complex student work. It can be used to evaluate various dimensions of mathematical activity such as problem solving, communication, use of mathematical language, reasoning, and number sense.

The following general 3-point rubric can be used with any problem in any section of this book. If you prefer, you may develop your own rubric to provide for a more specific assessment. When using a rubric, it is recommended that you discuss the criteria with your students ahead of time. Doing so will help students to understand what a complete response should include and will encourage them to take time to reflect on their answers.

3	The student accomplishes the purpose of the question or task. Understanding of the mathematics in the task is demonstrated, and the student is able to communicate his or her reasoning.
2	The student partially accomplishes the purpose of the question or task. Understanding of the mathematics may not be complete OR the student may not be able to communicate his or her reasoning adequately.
1	The student is not able to accomplish the purpose of the question or task. Understanding of the mathematics is fragmented, and the communication is vague or incomplete.

Section 1 What Number Makes Sense?

In this section, students are presented with problem situations from which numerical data are missing. A set of numbers is provided, and students determine where to place each number so the situation makes sense.

It is suggested that the teaching problem that follows be used as a whole-class activity.

The procedures outlined in the teaching problem will help students understand how to

a) carefully read the numerical situation,

b) decide which numbers to place in each blank,

c) determine whether or not the numbers they chose make sense.

The group interaction that occurs during the lesson will provide an opportunity for students to explain their thinking.

Consider having students work the first few problems that follow the teaching problem either with a partner or in a small group. After they have had a chance to become comfortable working with this type of problem, students can complete the remaining problems independently.

As they work through the exercises here, students practice computation and increase their repertoire of problem-solving skills. Students' reasoning skills are improved when they encounter a variety of ways to solve a problem. Be sure to engage students in a class discussion after each problem has been completed so they can hear ways of thinking about a problem that differ from their own.

Mathematical Skills

Teaching Problem
Number Sense, Percent

Problem 1
Number Sense

Problem 2
Fractions, Ratio/Proportion, Algebra

Problem 3
Time, Computation

Problem 4
Money, Fractions

Problem 5
Time, Fractions

Problem 6
Averages

Problem 7
Geometry, Perimeter, Area, Money

Problem 8
Time, Money

Problem 9
Money, Computation

Problem 10
Number Sense, Patterns

Magazine Ads

Teaching Goal

After participating in this lesson, students will be able to solve the problem by identifying and accurately placing the missing information. Students will also be able to explain their reasoning and defend their answers.

Problem

The April issue of *Wildlife Today* has _____ pages. Su Lee notices that of these, _____%, or _____ pages, are completely devoted to advertising. Of the remaining pages, _____%, or _____ pages, are more than half filled with ads. That leaves _____ pages with no advertising on them at all.

18   20 $33\frac{1}{3}$ 45   72   135

Teaching Plan

1. Present the problem to the students.
2. Have students read the problem individually or read it together as a class.
3. Ask students to think about the problem. Ask what they think they need to do to solve it.
4. Lead a whole-group discussion. Consider using the following questions as part of the discussion:

   What problem-solving strategy would you use to decide where to place the numbers? They may suggest strategies such as *Use Logical Reasoning* and *Guess and Check.*

What number makes the most sense for the total number of pages in the April issue of the magazine? They will probably choose 135, since that would represent the greatest number of pages.

What numbers would you consider as a possible percent of the total number of pages that might be completely devoted to advertising? They will probably choose the smaller numbers—18, 20, or $33\frac{1}{3}$.

Which of these percentages—18, 20, or $33\frac{1}{3}$—represents a number of pages that matches one of the choices? 18% of 135 would represent 24 pages, 20% of 135 would represent 27 pages, and $33\frac{1}{3}$% of 135 would represent 45 pages.

How would you determine the number of pages that "... are more than half filled with ads?" They will probably suggest that they would subtract the number of pages that are completely filled with ads, 45, from the total number of pages, 135, to get 90 pages.

5. Have students place the numbers in the blanks where they think they fit best.

What percent of the (90) pages are more than half filled with ads? How many pages is that? 20%; 18 pages

How did you determine the number of pages that have no advertising? They will probably say that they added 45 and 18 and then subtracted the sum, 63, from 135 to find that 72 pages had no advertising.

Explain how you know your answers are all correct? Explanations will vary.

This think-and-check problem-solving process, along with class discussion, allows students to use, extend, and communicate their reasoning and logic skills.

Name ....

Problem 1 **Music Cabinet**

Tyrone has a music cabinet full of CD's and videotapes. He has _______ more CD's than videos. If he buys _______ more CD, he will have exactly _______ times as many CD's as videos. Right now, he has _______ CD's and _______ videos in his cabinet.

75 38 37 2 1

1. First, read the problem.
2. Look at the numbers in the box.
3. Put the numbers in the blanks where you think they fit best.
4. Read the problem again. Do the numbers make sense?
5. Explain how you know you have the numbers in the correct blanks.

____

____

____

____

Name ....

Problem 2 **Trading Cards**

Michelle has a collection of ______ sports cards.

Of these, ______ are of soccer players and ______

are of hockey players. Of the remaining ______ cards,

there are ______ times as many cards of baseball

players as there are of football players. This means that

Michelle has ______ football player cards.

$\frac{1}{10}$	$\frac{3}{10}$	2	48	72	120

1. First, read the problem.
2. Look at the numbers in the box.
3. Put the numbers in the blanks where you think they fit best.
4. Read the problem again. Do the numbers make sense?
5. Explain how you know you have the numbers in the correct blanks.

____

____

____

____

____

____

Name ....

Problem 3 **Round Trips**

Mr. Henry has an ______-mile-long bus route in Philadelphia. He works a ______-hour shift, from ______:30 a.m. until ______:30 p.m., with ______ hour off for lunch. Each one-way trip takes him ______ minutes to complete, and he takes a ______-minute rest between trips. This means that he makes ______ round trips a day.

1	4	5	6	7	9	11	35

1. First, read the problem.
2. Look at the numbers in the box.
3. Put the numbers in the blanks where you think they fit best.
4. Read the problem again. Do the numbers make sense?
5. Explain how you know you have the numbers in the correct blanks.

____

____

____

____

____

____

Name ....

Problem 4 **Amount Still Due**

Brittany visited a used-instrument Web site to replace some of the instruments in her band. The site offers an electric keyboard for $________, an electric guitar for $________, and an acoustic guitar that costs ________ as much as the electric guitar. Brittany buys the electric keyboard and the acoustic guitar. If she makes a down payment of $________, she will still owe $________.

$\frac{1}{2}$	160	279	350	549

1. First, read the problem.
2. Look at the numbers in the box.
3. Put the numbers in the blanks where you think they fit best.
4. Read the problem again. Do the numbers make sense?
5. Explain how you know you have the numbers in the correct blanks.

____

____

____

____

Name ....

Problem 5 Commercial Breaks

A TV station has scheduled a made-for-TV movie for Monday night from 9:00 to 11:00. While the movie runs for exactly _______ minutes, the station plans to interrupt it with _______ commercials, each _______ minutes long, and _______ commercials, each _______ minutes long.

$1\frac{1}{2}$ 2 3 6 105

1. First, read the problem.
2. Look at the numbers in the box.
3. Put the numbers in the blanks where you think they fit best.
4. Read the problem again. Do the numbers make sense?
5. Explain how you know you have the numbers in the correct blanks.

____

____

____

____

____

____

Name ....

Problem 6 **Test Average**

Last semester, Kamal failed his first math test with a very low score of ______. He got a better score, ______, on his next test, but he still failed. After being tutored, Kamal passed his third test with a score of ______. He studied hard for his final exam and got his best score of all, a ______! This helped him to get a passing average of ______.

94	71	70	59	56

1. First, read the problem.
2. Look at the numbers in the box.
3. Put the numbers in the blanks where you think they fit best.
4. Read the problem again. Do the numbers make sense?
5. Explain how you know you have the numbers in the correct blanks.

____

____

____

____

____

Name ....

Problem 7 **White Wash**

Both sides of the white wall surrounding Larry's property need to be painted. The rectangular property measures _______ feet by _______ feet. The wall that surrounds it is _______ feet high. One gallon of paint costs $_______ and covers _______ square feet. So it will cost Larry $_______ for enough paint to cover the wall.

6	17.95	60	100	400	179.50

1. First, read the problem.
2. Look at the numbers in the box.
3. Put the numbers in the blanks where you think they fit best.
4. Read the problem again. Do the numbers make sense?
5. Explain how you know you have the numbers in the correct blanks.

____

____

____

____

____

____

Name ....

Problem 8 **Phone Charges**

On Saturday, Miss Lester phoned her sister in Los Angeles from her home in New York City. The conversation began at ______ p.m. and lasted until ______ p.m. Since Miss Lester's telephone company charges $______ a minute for calls made from ______ p.m. to ______ a.m. the next morning, she will be billed $______ for this call.

0.10	1.50	6	7	8:25	8:40

1. First, read the problem.
2. Look at the numbers in the box.
3. Put the numbers in the blanks where you think they fit best.
4. Read the problem again. Do the numbers make sense?
5. Explain how you know you have the numbers in the correct blanks.

____

____

____

____

____

Name ....

Problem 9 **Profit Margin**

Mary Ann makes brass pendants to sell at weekend craft fairs. Last month, she made _______ pendants, which cost her a total of $_______ to make. Last weekend, she sold _______ of these pendants for $_______ each. Her profit for the weekend was $_______.

236.25	110	40	35	9.50

1. First, read the problem.
2. Look at the numbers in the box.
3. Put the numbers in the blanks where you think they fit best.
4. Read the problem again. Do the numbers make sense?
5. Explain how you know you have the numbers in the correct blanks.

____

____

____

____

____

Name ....

Problem 10 **Grand Canyon Memories**

On his ______-day trip to the Grand Canyon, Carlos took ______ pictures. He took ______ pictures the first day, which was Tuesday. On each succeeding day, he took ______ more pictures than he did the day before. This means that he took ______ pictures on Wednesday and ______ on Thursday.

3	6	29	35	41	105

1. First, read the problem.
2. Look at the numbers in the box.
3. Put the numbers in the blanks where you think they fit best.
4. Read the problem again. Do the numbers make sense?
5. Explain how you know you have the numbers in the correct blanks.

____

____

____

____

____

Answer Key

Problem 1: Music Cabinet
37, 1, 2, 75, 38

Problem 2: Trading Cards
120, $\frac{1}{10}$, $\frac{3}{10}$, 72, 2, 48

Problem 3: Round Trips
11, 9, 7, 4, 35, 5, 6

Problem 4: Amount Still Due
549, 160, $\frac{1}{2}$, 350, 279

Problem 5: Commercial Breaks
105, 3, 2, 6, $1\frac{1}{2}$

Problem 6: Test Average
56, 59, 71, 94, 70

Problem 7: White Wash
60, 100, 6, 17.95, 400, 179.50

Problem 8: Phone Charges
8:25, 8:40, 0.10, 7, 6, 1.50

Problem 9: Profit Margin
40, 110, 35, 9.50, 236.25

Problem 10: Grand Canyon Memories
3, 105, 29, 6, 35, 41

Assessment Note
Student work on any of the problems in this section can be assessed using the 3-point rubric on page ix.

Section 2 What's Wrong?

Each problem that is presented in this section has been solved, but the solution is incorrect. An error has been made either in concept, interpretation, or computation. Students must identify the error that was made and find the correct solution to the problem.

It is recommended that the teaching problem that follows be used as a whole-class activity.

The procedures outlined in the teaching problem will take students through the process of

a) finding the correct solution to the problem,

b) identifying the error that was made.

Consider having students work the first few problems that follow the teaching problem either with a partner or in a small group. This will provide an opportunity for them to become comfortable working with this type of problem. The remaining pages might then be assigned for students to complete independently.

This section deals with error analysis. Each exercise offers an effective means for students to practice computation skills within a problem-solving context. Different strategies such as drawing diagrams or pictures, writing an equation, or creating a table or graph may be used to solve problems. By engaging in class discussion after a problem has been completed, students will be able to hear ways of solving problems that differ from their own. The group interaction that occurs during these discussions often leads to deeper mathematical understanding.

Mathematical Skills

Teaching Problem
Combinations

Problem 1
Ratio/Proportion, Algebra

Problem 2
Prime Factorization

Problem 3
Percent, Algebra

Problem 4
Measurement, Money

Problem 5
Geometry, Ratio

Problem 6
Algebra

Problem 7
Algebra

Problem 8
Fractions

Problem 9
Algebra, Guess and Check

Problem 10
Addition of Integers

Multiple Outfits

Teaching Goal

After participating in this lesson, students will be able to identify a reasoning error presented in the problem. Students will also choose a representation, either visual or numerical, and use it to solve the problem.

Problem

> Victoria has four shirts—1 yellow, 1 red, 1 with blue stripes, and 1 plaid. She also has three pairs of shorts—1 tan, 1 black, and 1 white. Victoria thinks that with these she can make 7 different shirt-and-shorts outfits.
>
> Victoria's thinking ▶ $4 + 3 = 7$

Teaching Plan

1. Present the problem to the students.
2. Have students read the problem.
3. Lead a whole-group discussion. Consider using the following questions as part of the discussion:

   How many different outfits can Victoria make if she wears the yellow shirt with a pair of shorts? 3

   How many different outfits can Victoria make if she wears the red shirt with a pair of shorts? 3

   How many different outfits can Victoria make if she wears the striped shirt with a pair of shorts? 3

   How many different outfits can Victoria make if she wears the plaid shirt with a pair of shorts? 3

 0-7622-1353-1

Victoria thought she could make only 7 different outfits. What is wrong with her thinking? She merely added the number of shirts to the number of shorts without considering the fact that each shirt can be paired with each of the three pairs of shorts to make an outfit.

How can you find Victoria's correct number of outfits? Students may suggest applying the *counting* principle, which states that if there are x outcomes for the first event and y outcomes for the second event, then the total number of possible outcomes can be found by multiplying x times y. Therefore, 4 shirts $\times$ 3 shorts = 12 outfits.

Does anyone have a different strategy? Some students may suggest drawing a *tree diagram* to illustrate the combinations that make up the 12 different outfits.

Shirts	Shorts	Outfits
yellow	tan	yellow/tan
	black	yellow/black
	white	yellow/white
red	tan	red/tan
	black	red/black
	white	red/white
striped	tan	striped/tan
	black	striped/black
	white	striped/white
plaid	tan	plaid/tan
	black	plaid/black
	white	plaid/white

You may wish to encourage students to use a specific type of representation to solve the different problems in this section. You may also have them try using multiple representations such as making a drawing and writing an equation to solve one or more of the problems.

Name ....

Problem 1 Monumental Problem

The Film-and-Screen Club is making a movie about ancient Egypt. For the big windstorm scene, the club needs scale models of the Great Sphinx and the Great Pyramid. For the Great Sphinx, which is actually about 66 feet high, they made a 12-inch-tall model. Now they need to make a model of the Great Pyramid. Since the Pyramid is actually about 450 feet high, Joseph figures that the model should be 2,475 inches tall.

Joseph's thinking ▶ $\frac{12}{66} = \frac{450}{x}$

$$12x = 66 \times 450$$

$$12x = 29{,}700$$

$$\frac{12x}{12} = \frac{29{,}700}{12}$$

$$x = 2{,}475$$

There is something wrong with Joseph's thinking.

1. Show how you would solve the problem.

2. Explain the error in Joseph's thinking.

____

____

Name ....

Problem 2 **Factor Tree**

Juanita was asked to prove that 36 is a composite number by writing it as a product of its prime factors. She made this factor tree and said that it showed the prime factors of 36 to be 3, 3, and 2. Then she wrote the prime factorization of 36 as $3 \times 3 \times 2$, or $3^2 \times 2$.

Juanita's thinking ▶

36

18 2

9 2

3 3 2

There is something wrong with Juanita's thinking.

1. Show how you would solve the problem.

2. Explain the error in Juanita's thinking.

Name ....

Problem 3 **Bigger Savings**

Kesha saw an ad for the Walk-About Radio in the Sunday paper. The ad said that, beginning Tuesday, the radio would be on sale for $33\frac{1}{3}\%$ off. Kesha bought the radio on Tuesday for \$30. She told her dad that by waiting until Tuesday to buy it, she had saved \$10 off its original price, which was \$40.

Kesha's thinking ▶ $33\frac{1}{3} \times \$30 = \frac{1}{3} \times \$30 = \$10$

$\$30 + \$10 = \$40$

There is something wrong with Kesha's thinking.

1. Show how you would solve the problem.

2. Explain the error in Kesha's thinking.

Name ....

Problem 4 **Figuring Fencing**

Ahmed wants to install a fence to separate the back of his 100-foot-wide property from the woods behind it. He told the clerk at Fortress Fencing that he needed 100 feet of fencing and enough fence posts for him to install every 10 feet. The clerk wrote up this order. The materials were soon delivered along with this bill.

Fortress Fencing	
10 fence posts at $14.50 each	$145.00
100 feet of fencing at $5.00 per foot	500.00
Nails and binders	25.00
Subtotal	$670.00
Tax	43.55
Total	$713.55

There is something wrong with the clerk's thinking.

1. Show how you would solve the problem.

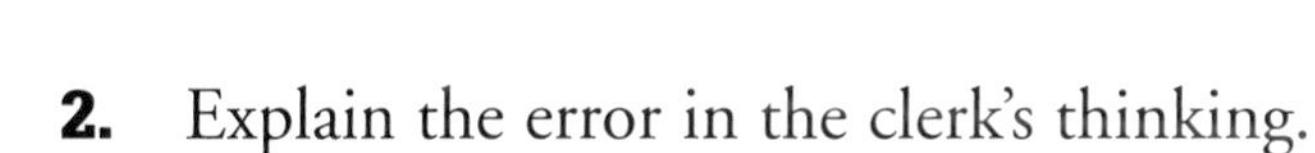

2. Explain the error in the clerk's thinking.

Name ....

Problem 5 **What's Her Angle?**

Tamara has a magnifying glass through which objects appear 3 times their actual size. One day she used a protractor to draw a 14° angle. Then she picked up her magnifying glass, placed it over the angle, and decided that what she saw through the glass was a 42° angle.

Tamara's thinking ▶ $3 \times 14° = 42°$

There is something wrong with Tamara's thinking.

1. Show how you would solve the problem.

2. Explain the error in Tamara's thinking.

 0-7622-1353-1

Name ....

Problem 6 "Heavy" News

Jamal's teacher assigned this problem about the weight of the newspapers at a recycling center. Jamal said that the answer to the problem was 1,333.33 pounds.

- The number of pounds of newspapers in Bin 1 is one-third the number of pounds in Bin 2.
- The number of pounds in Bin 3 is twice the number of pounds in Bin 2.
- The total weight of the newspaper in all three bins is 40,000 pounds.
- How many pounds of newspaper are in Bin 1?

Jamal's thinking ▶ If B = number of pounds in Bin 2

Then $B \div 3$ = number of pounds in Bin 1

And $2B$ = number of pounds in Bin 3

$$B + (B \div 3) + 2B = 40{,}000$$

$$3B + B + 6B = 40{,}000$$

$$10B = 40{,}000$$

$$B = 4{,}000$$

So, Bin 1 contains $B \div 3$, or $(4{,}000 \div 3)$, which equals 1,333.33 pounds of newspapers.

There is something wrong with Jamal's thinking.

1. Show how you would solve the problem.

2. Explain the error in Jamal's thinking.

Name ....

Problem 7 **Perennial Garden**

Last year, Marsha gave Grandma 7 plants for her herb garden. This year, Uncle Ned doubled Grandma's number of herb plants, which brought the total number of plants to 24. Marsha figures that there must have been 17 plants in the garden before she and Uncle Ned gave Grandma the additional ones.

Marsha's thinking ▶ Let P = number of plants that Grandma started with.

$$2(P + 7) = 24$$
$$2P + 14 = 48$$
$$2P = 34$$
$$P = 17$$

There is something wrong with Marsha's thinking.

1. Show how you would solve the problem.

2. Explain the error in Marsha's thinking.

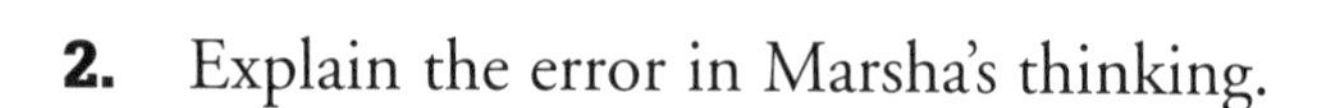

Name ....

Problem 8 **Sizing Up Slices**

The Chens ordered a large (12″) mushroom pizza and a medium (10″) pepperoni pizza. Each of the pizzas was cut into 8 equal slices. John ate 2 slices of the mushroom pizza. Ming ate 2 slices of the pepperoni pizza. When Mrs. Chen asked who had eaten more pizza, Ming said that they had each eaten the same amount.

Ming's thinking ▶ $\frac{1}{4}$ of the mushroom pizza $=$ $\frac{1}{4}$ of the pepperoni pizza

There is something wrong with Ming's thinking.

1. Show how you would solve the problem.

2. Explain the error in Ming's thinking.

____

____

____

____

Name ....

Problem 9 **Stamp Collection**

Lana told Paul that she had 46 stamps in her collection. She said she had 16 more U.S. stamps than foreign stamps. Then she challenged Paul to figure out how many U.S. stamps she actually had. Paul decided that she had 30.

Paul's thinking ▶ Let x = number of foreign stamps in the collection

$x + 16 = 46$

$x = 30$

So, I figure there are 30 foreign stamps and 16 U.S. stamps.

There is something wrong with Paul's thinking.

1. Show how you would solve the problem.

2. Explain what's wrong with Paul's thinking.

____

____

____

____

Name ....

Problem 10 **River Rides**

Reva gives environmental tours of the river. The tour boat leaves the dock and goes 8 kilometers upstream. Then Reva turns the boat around and goes 3 kilometers downstream before stopping to point out wildlife. A passenger decides that the boat is now 11 kilometers from the dock.

Passenger's thinking ▶ $8 + 3 = 11$

There is something wrong with the passenger's thinking.

1. Show how you would solve the problem.

2. Explain the error in the passenger's thinking.

____

____

____

____

 0-7622-1353-1

Answer Key

Problem 1: Monumental Problem

Joseph's ratio for the Great Sphinx is

$$\frac{12}{66} = \frac{\text{height of model}}{\text{height of monument}}.$$

The right side of his proportion should have reflected this same ratio of height of model to height of monument. Instead, Joseph mistakenly compared the height of the monument to the height of the model. The correct proportion and its solution follows.

$$\frac{12}{66} = \frac{x}{540}$$
$$66x = 12 \times 540 = 6{,}480$$
$$x = 98.18$$
$$x \cong 98$$

So the height of the model of the Great Pyramid should be about 98 inches tall.

Problem 2: Factor Tree

After first identifying the factors of 36 as being 18 and 2, Juanita went on to factor 18, but she forgot to bring the 2 down to the next level in her factor tree. Her factor tree should have looked like this one.

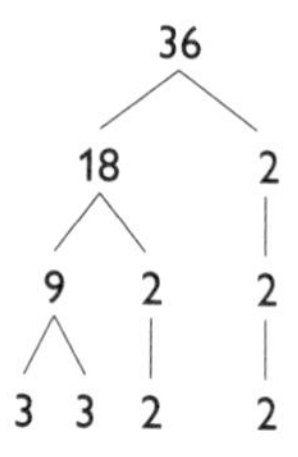

So the prime factorization of 36 is correctly $3 \times 3 \times 2 \times 2$, or $3^2 \times 2^2$.

Problem 3: Bigger Savings

In trying to find the original price of the radio, Kesha's mistake is that she found one third of the sale price, \$30, and added that amount to the \$30. She should have, instead, computed as follows.

If x = original price of radio
Then $x - 33\frac{1}{3}x$ = sale price

$$x - \tfrac{1}{3}x = 30$$
$$\tfrac{2}{3}x = 30$$
$$2x = 90$$
$$x = 45$$

So the original price of the radio was \$45.

Problem 4: Figuring Fencing

The clerk did not order enough fence posts.

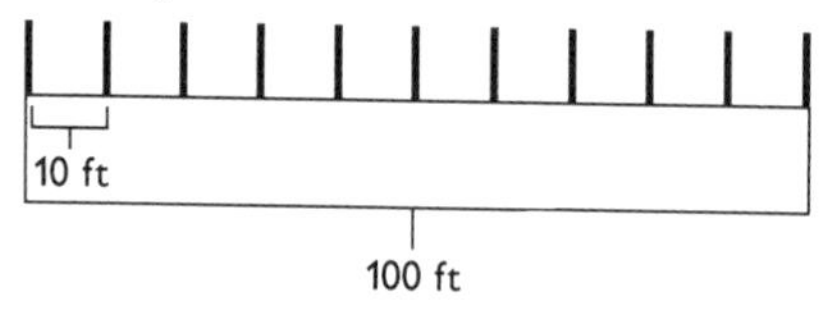

The diagram shows that 11 posts, not 10, would be needed for the job. Cost of 11 posts is \$159.50. Subtotal is \$684.50. Rate of tax is 6.5%. \$684.50 × 6.5% is \$44.49. Total is \$728.99.

Problem 5: What's Her Angle?

If Tamara looked at a 14° angle through a magnifying glass, the sides of the angle would appear longer, but the size of the angle would remain the same.

Problem 6: "Heavy" News

Jamal set up the equation properly, but in solving it he failed to multiply the right side of the equation by 3. The correct solution follows:

$$B + (B \div 3) + 2B = 40{,}000$$
$$3B + B + 6B = 120{,}000$$
$$10B = 120{,}000$$
$$B = 12{,}000$$

So, Bin 1 contains $B \div 3$, or $(12{,}000 \div 3) = 4{,}000$ pounds.

Problem 7: Perennial Garden

Marsha mistakenly multiplied on the right side of the equation. The correct solution follows.

$$2(P + 7) = 24$$
$$2P + 14 = 24$$
$$2P = 10$$
$$P = 5$$

Problem 8: Sizing Up Slices

By eating $\frac{1}{4}$ of the larger (mushroom) pizza, John had a larger portion than Ming had when she ate $\frac{1}{4}$ of the smaller (pepperoni) pizza.

Problem 9: Stamp Collection

Paul's solution would have been correct if Lana had 16 U.S. stamps. But, in fact, she had ". . . 16 *more* U.S. stamps than foreign ones." The correct solution, where x = foreign stamps, follows.

$$x + (x + 16) = 46$$
$$2x + 16 = 46$$
$$2x = 30$$
$$x = 15 \text{ foreign stamps}$$
$$15 + 16 = 31 \text{ U.S. stamps}$$

The correct solution could also be found by using the guess-and-check strategy. For example:

Numbers of Stamps: U.S./Foreign	Difference
40 and 6	34 more U.S.
35 and 11	24 more U.S.
30 and 16	14 more U.S.
31 and 15	16 more U.S.

Problem 10: River Rides

The passenger forgot how to add two integers with different signs. The correct solution is $8 + {}^{-}3 = 5$. They are now 5 km from the dock.

Assessment Note

Student work on any of the problems in this section can be assessed using the 3-point rubric on page ix.

Section 3 What Would You Do?

OPEN-ENDED PROBLEMS ARE PRESENTED in this section. In each case, after finding an answer, students are asked to support their solution.

These problems give students the opportunity to use their prior knowledge as a foundation on which to build and strengthen their skills. Both computation and problem-solving abilities are engaged.

Consider using the teaching problem format with the first few problems in the section. The next few might then be solved within small groups, and the remaining problems completed on an individual basis.

Group discussions about solutions provide an important forum for a valuable exchange of ideas. These discussions allow students to practice effective communication of their own mathematical thinking and to gain insights and understanding through listening to the solution strategies of others.

Mathematical Skills

Teaching Problem
Data Analysis, Graphs, Time

Problem 1
Money, Computation

Problem 2
Percent, Interest, Money

Problem 3
Money

Problem 4
Geometry, Fractions

Problem 5
Money, Measurement, Time

Problem 6
Money, Fractions

Problem 7
Geometry, Area, Perimeter

Problem 8
Percent, Commission, Money

Problem 9
Decimals, Money

Problem 10
Logic, Computation

Time Flies

Teaching Goal

After participating in this lesson, students will be able to use a number of tools such as their experiences, prior knowledge, and individual preferences to solve the problem. Students will also be able to support their answers using logic and reasoning.

Problem

> As a new member of the Astronomy Club you have been asked to make a presentation about the changes in the hours of daylight during the last two weeks of April. You did some research and found out that on April 13 the sun rose at 6:26 a.m. and set at 7:37 p.m. On each of the remaining days of the month, the sun rose $1\frac{1}{2}$ minutes earlier and set 1 minute later than it did the day before.

Teaching Plan

1. Present the problem to the students.
2. Have students read the problem.
3. Lead a whole-group discussion. Ask:

   How would you display your data for your presentation? Groups, or pairs, of students could present the data in various forms, such as in a table or in a double-line or double-bar graph.

4. Discuss each of the various types of presentations that students submit. Consider using the following questions as part of the discussion. Note that the answers are based on a count of *17 days* from April 13 to April 30. Inasmuch as Daylight Savings Time goes into effect in April, since the day on which it falls varies from year to year, we have purposefully not mentioned it in this problem. However, you may wish to have your students take into account the actual day on which Daylight Savings Time begins this year and then work the problem based on that date.

How much daylight was there on April 13? 13 hours and 11 minutes

On April 30, what time was sunrise? 6:00:30 a.m.

On April 30, what time was sunset? 7:54 p.m.

How much daylight was there on April 30? 13 hours, 53 minutes, 30 seconds

How much more daylight time was there on April 30 than on April 13? 42 minutes, 30 seconds more

---

Since the problems in this section are somewhat open-ended, there may be a variety of strategies and solutions. It is important to encourage the students to choose a solution that they can defend.

Name ....

Problem 1 **Cable TV**

Garden Cable TV has come to your area. Your family needs to decide which channels to order for a monthly package. Basic Service can be ordered alone, but none of the other channels can be ordered *without* Basic Service. Your parents have agreed to spend up to $40 a month for cable. The company's rates are as shown.

GARDEN CABLE TV Monthly Rates	
Service	**Cost**
Basic Service	$ 6.95
Best Movies	$13.95
Sports Channel	$14.95
Country Music	$ 9.95
News-All-Day	$ 6.50
Cartoon Channel	$10.95

1. Which channels would you choose for a monthly package?

____

____

____

____

2. Explain your choices.

____

____

____

____

____

____

Name ....

Problem 2 **Birthday Money**

Suppose you get $100 for your birthday. You know that if you spend it, it will be gone, but if you put it into a savings account, it can earn more money for you. The signs below show the interest rates at three of your local banks and the gift you receive for opening an account.

Long Island National Bank	Homeville Interstate Bank	Park Avenue Bank
Pays 5% on money in account at the end of the year	Pays $4\frac{1}{2}$% on money in account at the end of the year	Pays $5\frac{1}{2}$% on money in account at the end of the year
Gift of daily planner ($6 value) for opening a new account	Gift of a calculator ($10 value) for opening a new account	Gift of computer mouse pad ($2 value) for opening a new account

1. In which bank would you save your money? Which factor seems more important, a bank's rate of interest or the gift you get for opening a new account?

____

____

____

2. Explain how you made your choice.

____

____

____

Name ....

Problem 3 **Chess Tournament**

There are 31 finalists in the city-wide chess tournament. Your job is to set up the tournament schedule. You have $1,200 to award as prizes.

1. Decide how many rounds of play there will be. (Assume that there will be no draws.)

2. How many prizes will you give out? How much will each prize be worth?

Name ....

Problem 4 **Dinner Dilemma**

Jenna had just made lasagna in a 10-in. × 16-in. pan for herself and three friends. No sooner had she cut the lasagna into four equal slices than the doorbell rang. Another friend was at the door. She invited him to join them for dinner to have an equal share of the lasagna.

1. You can see how Jenna cut the four equal slices. Draw lines to show how she could cut the lasagna so that everyone gets an equal share.

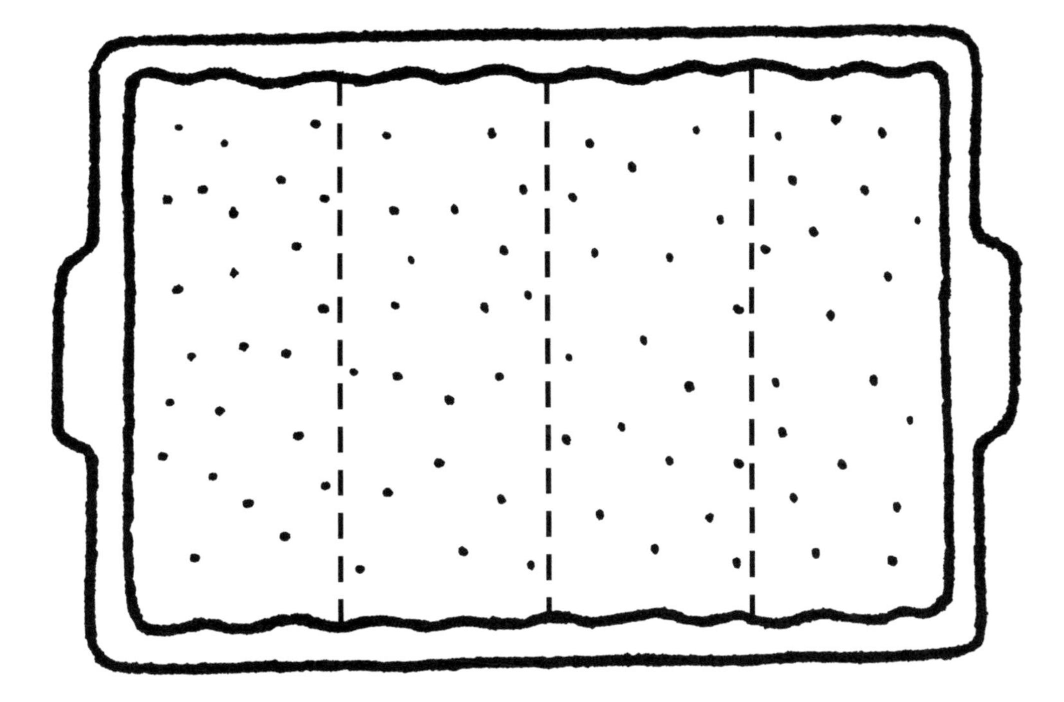

2. Explain why your way of cutting the lasagna works.

____

____

____

© Wright Group/McGraw-Hill 0-7622-1353-1

Name ....

Problem 5 **Way to Go**

Mr. and Mrs. Burwasser and their two children, ages 9 and 11, are planning to attend a family reunion 450 miles from home. They will be away for a total of 8 days. After checking both airline and automobile-rental prices, they narrowed down their means of travel to these two.

1. Which means of travel would you recommend that the Burwassers take to the reunion? (Don't forget to consider possible extra costs, such as the cost of traveling to and from the airport and the cost of gasoline.)

____

____

2. Explain your choice of recommendation.

____

____

____

Name ....

Problem 6 **Pricing Tickets**

The members of a local drama club are meeting to decide on the ticket prices for their winter production. The total cost of the production—including costumes, scenery, printing the tickets and programs, and advertising the show—comes to $3,700. The club is hoping to make a profit of at least $3,000.

There will be two performances of the show. They will be held at the high school auditorium, which seats up to 360 people in its three sections. Half the seats are in the center section of the orchestra. One-third of the seats are in the balcony. The rest of the seats are along the sides.

1. How do you think the club should price the tickets for this show?

____

____

____

____

2. Explain your decisions.

____

____

____

____

____

Name ....

Problem 7 **Fair Design**

Your town's annual fair will be held on the town green. Your class has been asked to figure out how to arrange the booths. The dimensions and configuration of the town green are shown below. The chart shows the number of booths you need to arrange and the size of each.

Number of Booths	Size of Booths
20	9 ft × 12 ft
20	15 ft × 12 ft
15	21 ft × 12 ft
15	30 ft × 12 ft

1. Draw your layout of the booths on this diagram.

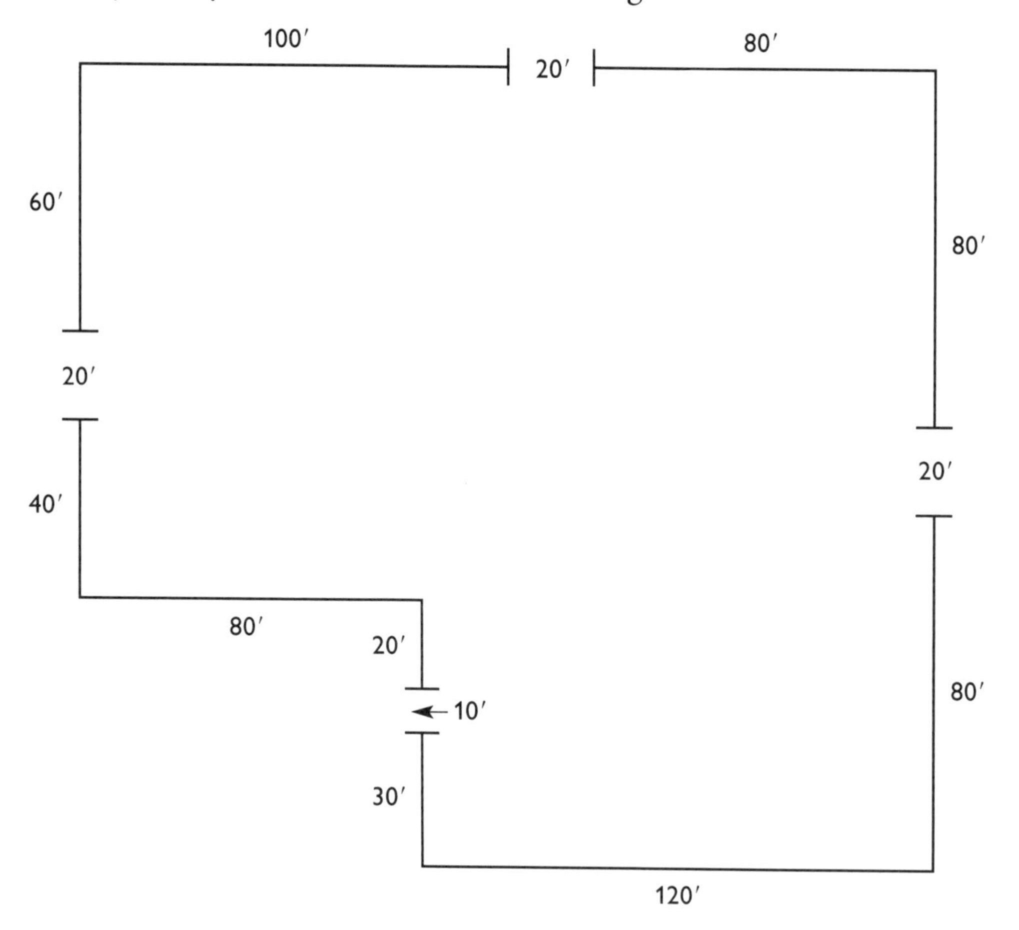

2. Explain your decisions.

____

____

Name ....

Problem 8 **Car Sales**

You have been offered a sales job at each of three new-car dealerships. Just as the average price of a new car varies from one dealership to the next, a salesperson's base salary and percent of commission vary as well. The chart shows this.

Dealership	Average Price of Car	Base Salary Plus Percent of Commission on All Sales
Marvel	$18,000	$1,600/month + 1%
Tony's	$32,000	$800/month + 3%
Parker	$21,000	$1,200/month + 2%

1. For which dealership would you like to work?

____

____

____

____

2. Explain how you made your choice.

____

____

____

____

____

Name ....

Problem 9 **Power Up**

As a resident of your state you may now choose your energy supplier from a list of three—the Everthere Power Company, the Never-Fail Power Company, and the Light 'n Brite Power Company. The chart shows each company's monthly fee and price per kilowatt-hour.

Company	Monthly Fee	Price/Kilowatt-Hour
Everthere Power	$5.75 for first 100 kilowatt-hours	$.10 per kilowatt-hour over 100
Never-Fail Power	$6.75 for first 100 kilowatt-hours	$.085 per kilowatt-hour over 100
Light 'n Brite	$10.00	$.055 per kilowatt-hour

1. Which company is your choice?

____

2. Explain your choice.

____

____

____

____

____

____

Name ....

Problem 10 **Lobsterfest**

Suppose you spend a one-week internship on a lobster boat in Maine. Every day the boat leaves the harbor and the lobsterman visits his traps, pulling each trap from the ocean and emptying it into the hull of his boat and then resetting it and dropping it back into the ocean. The map shows how the traps are arranged and the number of yards between them. You notice that every day the lobsterman visits his traps in alphabetical order (according to how they are labeled on the map), from A to B to C to D to E to F to G.

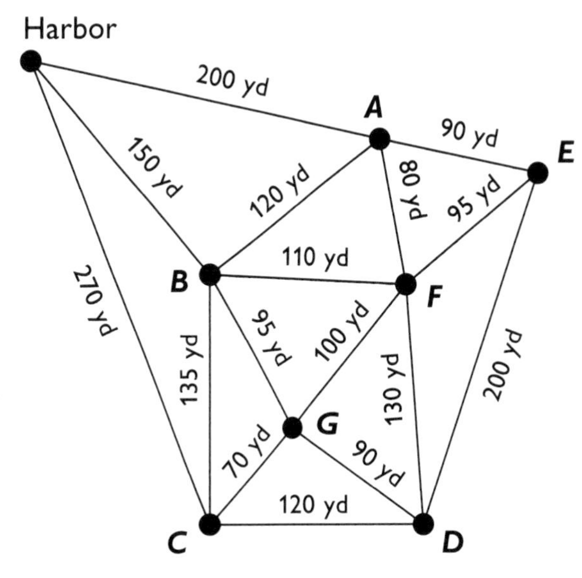

1. At the end of the week, the lobsterman asks you to suggest the order in which you would visit the traps each day. What order would you use?

____

____

____

2. Explain your answer.

____

____

____

____

Answer Key

Problem 1: Cable TV
Answers will vary. Students should subtract the \$6.95 cost of basic service from \$40 to realize that their choices of channels may add up to no more than \$33.05.

Problem 2: Birthday Money
Answers will vary.

Problem 3: Chess Tournament
There will be five rounds. Students should realize that there must be a "bye" for the first round only. The player who is the bye does not play in the first round, but plays in the second round against one of the winners of the first round.

Round 1: 30 players
15 games

Round 2: 16 players including bye
8 games

Round 3: 8 players
4 games

Round 4: 4 players
2 games

Round 5: 2 players
1 game

Problem 4: Dinner Dilemma
Answers will vary. One possibility is for Jenna to make four equally spaced cuts along the 10″ side. This would yield a total of twenty 2″-by-4″ pieces. The five friends could each have 4 of these pieces.

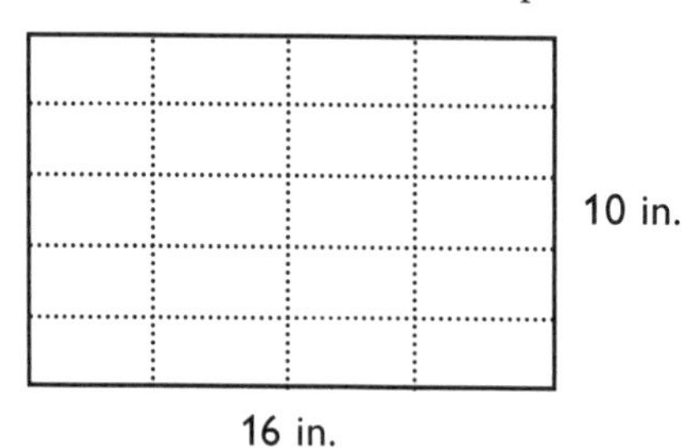

Problem 5: Way to Go
Answers will vary. Encourage students to consider current gas prices and unstated possible "hidden" costs, such as airport taxes and the cost of parking at the airport.

Problem 6: Pricing Tickets
Answers will vary. Students must realize that in order for the club to make a profit of \$3,000, ticket sales must total at least \$3,700 (costs) + \$3,000 (profit), or \$6,700.

Problem 7: Fair Design
Answers will vary. Since the area of the town green is 35,200 square feet and the total area of the booths is 15,840 square feet, there are many possible arrangements for the booths. Be sure that students consider leaving room between the booths for aisles.

Problem 8: Car Sales
Answers will vary based on students' assumptions of how many cars they might sell at each dealership.

Problem 9: Power Up
Answers will vary. Students should be allowed enough time to collect data that may be available about the number of kilowatt-hours of electricity that their families typically use in a month.

Problem 10: Lobsterfest
Answers will vary. Students may continue to use the same alphabetical order that the lobsterman uses, or they may offer an alternative order based on efficiency (least distance) or design.

Assessment Note
Student work on any of the problems in this section can be assessed using the 3-point rubric on page ix.

Section 4 What Questions Can You Answer?

IN THIS SECTION, STUDENTS ARE PRESENTED with situations that include numerical data and are asked to generate questions that can be answered from the data. There is a natural integration of language arts and mathematics as students analyze information, formulate and record their questions, and then find the answers to the questions they've created.

It is recommended that the teaching problem that follows be used as a whole-class activity.

The procedures outlined in the teaching problem will help students understand how to

a) identify the information that is given in the problem,
b) determine what kinds of questions can be constructed from the data,
c) find a solution to the questions posed.

Consider having students work the first few problems that follow the teaching problem with a partner or in small groups. This will allow them to brainstorm ideas to generate as many questions as possible. They can select their best questions to record on the student page and then work together to find the solutions. The remaining problems might then be assigned for students to work independently.

After students have completed working on a problem, be sure to discuss the questions generated as well as the answers. Such discussion can provide a valuable opportunity for students to hear the variety of questions posed.

Mathematical Skills

Teaching Problem
Geometry, Angles

Problem 1
Venn Diagrams

Problem 2
Geometry, Area, Perimeter

Problem 3
Unit Pricing, Decimals, Ratio/Proportion

Problem 4
Double Bar Graph

Problem 5
Time, Fractions

Problem 6
Pie Graphs, Percent, Ratio

Problem 7
Data Analysis, Statistics

Problem 8
Statistics

Problem 9
Line Graph

Problem 10
Computation, Percent

A Matter of Degrees

Teaching Goal

After participating in this lesson, students should be cognizant of the breadth and depth of questions that can be constructed with given data. They should also be able to find answers to questions they pose.

Problem

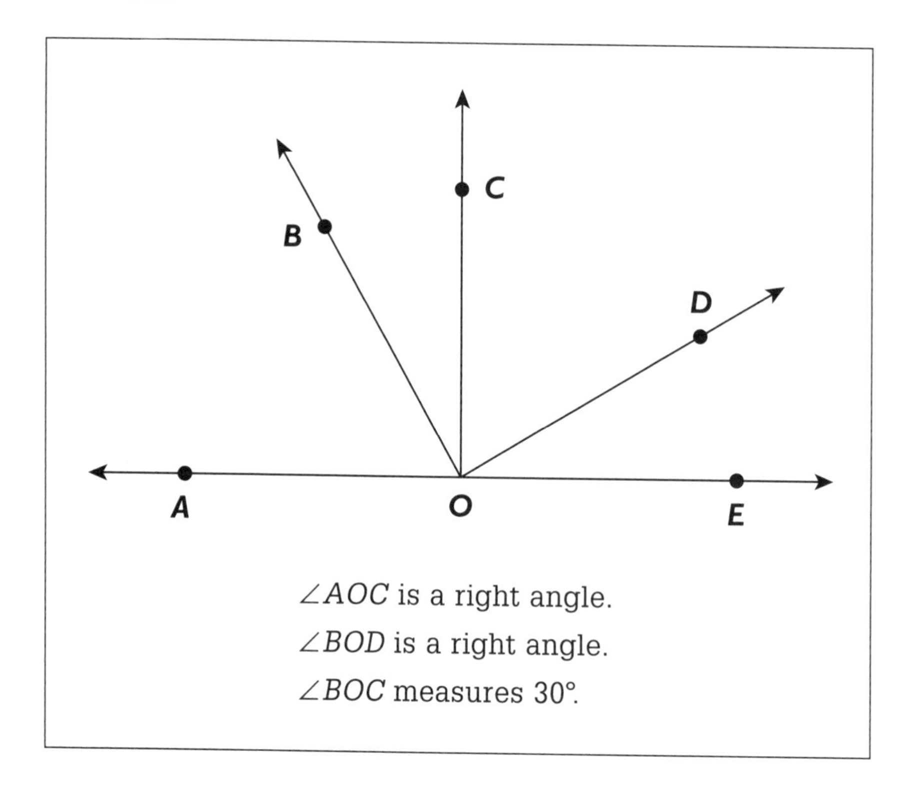

$\angle AOC$ is a right angle.

$\angle BOD$ is a right angle.

$\angle BOC$ measures 30°.

Teaching Plan

1. Display the above figure on the overhead projector or draw it on a chalkboard or white board.
2. Ask students to read the information.
3. Have one student come to the board and mark the angles according to the given information; that is, marking angles *AOC* and *BOD* with right-angle symbols and marking angle *BOC* as having 30°.

4. Lead a discussion with the whole class using the following questions as part of the discussion:

   What information are you given? The number of degrees in three of the angles in the diagram—90°, 90°, and 30°.

   When you see a diagram of angles like this, the teacher usually asks some questions about the diagram. Today you are going to get a chance to be the teacher and think of some questions that could be answered with the given information. Can you think of one such question? One question that might be suggested is, "How many degrees are there in $\angle COE$"? Record students' questions on the board. Although each problem asks for two questions, encourage students to generate as many questions as possible including the following:

   What is the measure of $\angle COD$? 60°

   What is the measure of $\angle BOA$? 60°

   What is the measure of $\angle DOE$? 30°

   What is the measure of $\angle AOE$? 180°

5. After a variety of questions have been generated, invite students to find their solutions.

   How can you be sure that $\angle COD$ measures 60°? It is given that $\angle BOD$ is a right angle and that $\angle BOC$ measures 30°. Since $\angle BOC$ is contained in $\angle BOD$, then $90° - 30° = 60°$.

   How can you be sure that $\angle AOE$ measures 180°? Angle *AOE* represents the sum of the two adjacent right angles, so $90° + 90° = 180°$.

Almost all students will be able to achieve some level of success with this lesson. The sophistication of questions posed depends on the developmental level of each student.

Section 4

Name ....

Problem 1 **Music Groups**

A music teacher in charge of a band, a chorus, and an orchestra made this Venn diagram to record the numbers of students in his music groups.

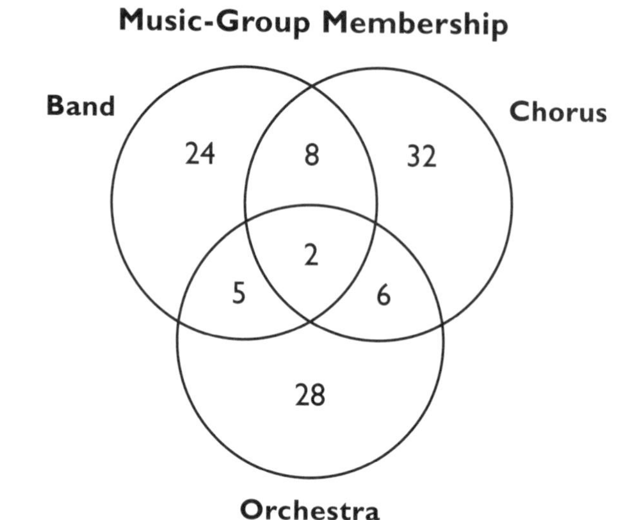

Write two questions you can answer from the data shown in the Venn diagram.

1. ______________________________

____

____

2. ______________________________

____

____

3. Find the answer to your first question. Show your work.

____

____

____

____

Name ....

Problem 2 **Geometric Shape**

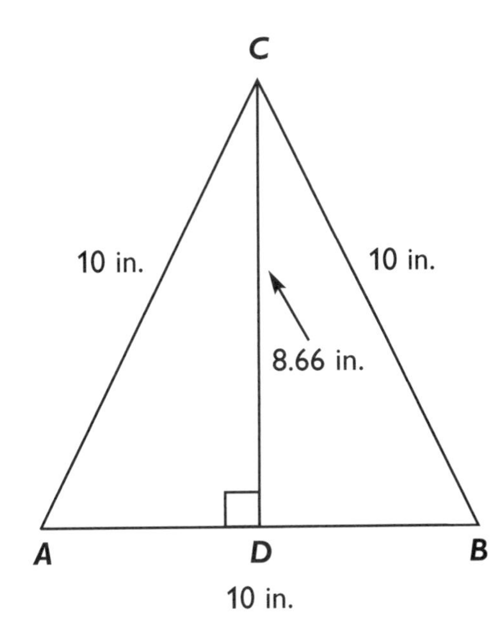

Write two questions you can answer about the figure.

1. ______________________________

____

____

2. ______________________________

____

____

3. Find the answer to your first question. Show your work.

____

____

____

____

Name ....

Problem 3 **Super Sales**

The SuperMart sends out a flier announcing its weekly specials. Here are some of the products the store has on sale this week.

Write two questions you can answer about the data given in the flier.

1. ____

____

____

2. ____

____

____

3. Find the answer to your first question. Show your work.

____

____

____

Name ....

Problem 4 **Skating Survey**

A group of seventh-graders have petitioned for a skate park to be built in their town. They took a survey of how many kids skated and skateboarded on Main Street every weekday from 3:00 and 7:00. Here is the graph of the results of their survey, which they will present to the Town Council.

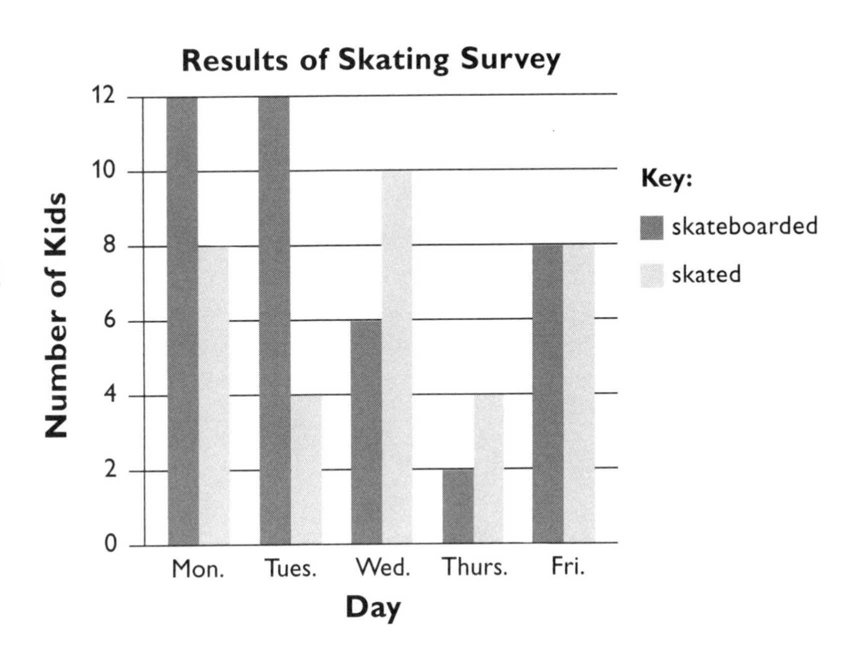

Write two questions you can answer about the results of the skating survey.

1. ____

____

____

2. ____

____

____

3. Find the answer to your first question. Show your work.

____

____

____

Name ....

Problem 5 **Bird Watching**

After school let out for the summer, Marissa spent the week recording the numbers of birds that came to her backyard. Here is her record.

Kinds of Birds		How Many I Saw
Swallows:	Tree Swallow	2
	Bank Swallow	3
	Barn Swallow	3
Thrushes:	Hermit Thrush	15
	Wood Thrush	5
Sparrows:	Grasshopper Sparrow	4
	Henslow's Sparrow	9
Warblers:	Blue-winged Warbler	1
	Golden-winged Warbler	1
	Nashville Warbler	7
Wrens:	House Wren	19
	Marsh Wren	7

Write two questions you can answer about Marissa's bird-watching record.

1. ______________________________

____

____

2. ______________________________

____

____

3. Find the answer to your first question. Show your work.

____

____

____

Name ....

Problem 6 **Pie Charts**

The pie charts shows the percentages of specialty pizzas sold at Pizza Palazzo in September and October.

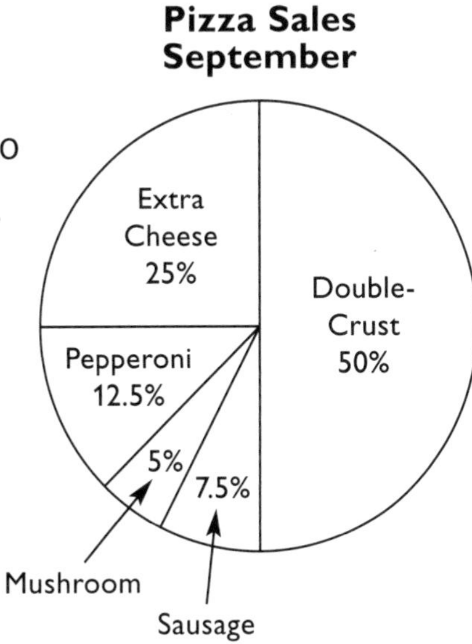

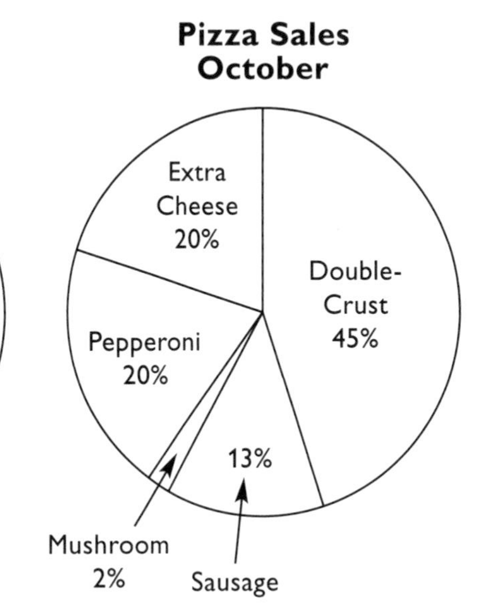

Write two questions you can answer about the pie charts.

1. ______________________________

____

____

2. ______________________________

____

____

3. Find the answer to your first question. Show your work.

____

____

____

____

Name ....

Problem 7 **Players' Stats**

Here are statistics about some of the players on the Osterville Ospreys basketball team.

Name	Age	Height	Weight
Rasheed Williams	21	6′2″	190 lb
Lamar George	19	6′1″	192 lb
Tony Johnson	23	6′6″	212 lb
Sonny Albert	25	5′11″	178 lb
Mario Zapata	26	5′9″	168 lb
Marty Lenox	21	6′0″	208 lb
Mike James	25	6′3″	214 lb

Write two questions you can answer about the statistics in the chart.

1. ______________________________

____

____

2. ______________________________

____

____

3. Find the answer to your first question. Show your work.

____

____

____

Name ....

Problem 8 **Great Lakes**

The table lists the area of each of the Great Lakes.

Lake	Area (in square miles)
Erie	9,910
Huron	23,010
Michigan	22,300
Ontario	7,540
Superior	31,700

Write two questions you can answer about the statistics in the table.

1. ______________________________

____

____

2. ______________________________

____

____

3. Find the answer to your first question. Show your work.

____

____

____

____

____

Name ....

Problem 9 **Car Values**

The graph shows the decreasing value of a new car.

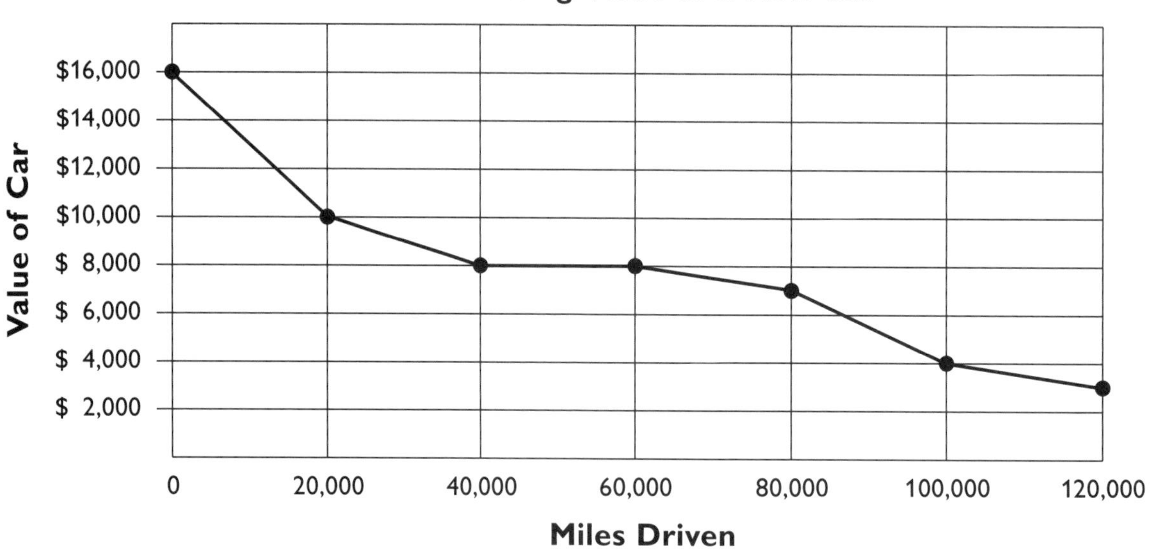

Write two questions you can answer about the line graph.

1. ____

____

____

2. ____

____

____

3. Find the answer to your first question. Show your work.

____

____

____

Name ....

Problem 10 **Monday Night TV**

One Monday night, the Highest TV-Ratings Company took a telephone survey. They asked 1,000 families which TV shows they were watching. Here are the responses they got.

TV Show	Number of Responses*
Comedy Club	345
Football Game	193
Monday Night Movie	253
Seven's a Crowd	70
Other Programs	105
(Not Watching TV)	34

(*Every response represents 140 actual viewers.)

Write two questions you can answer about the telephone survey.

1. ____

____

____

2. ____

____

____

3. Find the answer to your first question. Show your work.

____

____

____

Answer Key

In this section students write questions that can be answered with the information given. This answer key includes typical questions that might be written by students. Many other questions are possible.

Problem 1: Music Groups
Possible questions
How many music students are in the band? (39)

How many music students are in the chorus and orchestra but not the band? (6)

How many music students are in all three groups? (2)

How many music students are not in the orchestra? (64)

Problem 2: Geometric Shape
Possible questions
What is the perimeter of triangle *ABC*? (30 inches)

What is the area of triangle *ABC*? (43.3 square inches)

ABC is what kind of triangle? (equilateral, equiangular)

What is the area of triangle *ADC*? (21.65 square inches)

Problem 3: Super Sales
Possible questions
How much would an 18-ounce bottle of Glow, a 10-ounce box of Crispy, and a 2.1-pound pack of apricots cost? ($12.72)

Which is the better buy, the 18-ounce bottle of Glow or the or the 24-ounce bottle? (The 24-ounce bottle is the better buy. It costs $.29 per ounce while the 18-ounce bottle costs $.32 per ounce.)

Is the package containing the greater amount always the better buy? (No, the 3.3-pound pack of apricots costs $2.45 per pound while the 2.1-pound pack costs $2.37 per pound.)

Problem 4: Skating Survey
Possible questions
How many more kids skateboarded than skated on Tuesday? (8)

How many skateboarders and skaters were there altogether on Friday? (16)

How many kids skateboarded and skated during the week? (74)

Problem 5: Bird Watching
Possible questions
How many swallows did Marissa see? (8)

How many fewer Marsh Wrens did she see than House Wrens? (12)

How many thrushes and sparrows did she see altogether? (33)

Problem 6: Pie Graphs
Possible questions
In September there were twice as many extra-cheese pizzas sold as what kind of pizza? (pepperoni)

For which kind of pizza was there a 5.5% increase in sales from September to October? (sausage)

What was the ratio of double-crust pizzas to pepperoni sold in September? (4 to 1)

Problem 7: Players' Stats
Possible questions
What is the average height of the team members? (6′1″)

What is the average age of the team members? (23 years)

What is the average weight of the team members? (194.6 pounds)

Problem 8: Great Lakes
Possible questions
What is the total area of all five lakes? (94,460 square miles)

What is the average area of the five lakes? (18,892 square miles)

Lake Michigan occupies what percent of the total area of the lakes? (24%)

Problem 9: Car Values
Possible questions
When does the value of the car decrease the most? (during the first 20,000 miles)

When does the value of the car decrease the least? (between 40,000 and 60,000 miles)

What is the value of the car once it has been driven 100,000 miles? ($4,000)

Problem 10: Monday Night TV
Possible questions
How many actual viewers were watching the football game? (27,020)

How many more actual viewers were watching *Comedy Club* than the *Monday Night Movie*? (12,880)

What percent of the people surveyed were watching *Seven's a Crowd*? (7%)

Assessment Note
Student work on any of the problems in this section can be assessed using the 3-point rubric on page ix.

Section 5 What's Missing?

IN THIS SECTION, STUDENTS ARE PRESENTED with problems that cannot be solved because an important piece of information has been omitted. Students must identify what is missing, supply appropriate data, and then solve the problem.

It is recommended that the teaching problem that follows be used as a whole-class activity.

The procedures outlined in the teaching problem will help students understand how to

a) identify the question that is asked,
b) determine the piece of information that is missing,
c) supply a number or other data that will enable them to solve the problem.

After the teaching problem, it is suggested that students work with a partner or in a small group, especially for the initial lessons. Once the students are comfortable with the procedures, the remaining problems can be worked independently.

Group discussion of problems throughout this section is important, even after students are working independently. Because there is a wide range of data that students can supply to solve each problem, interesting discussions based on the specific data chosen are possible. Each different piece of missing information supplied by a student produces a different solution.

Mathematical Skills

Teaching Problem
Geometry, Area

Problem 1
Probability

Problem 2
Money, Percent

Problem 3
Time, Number Sense

Problem 4
Money, Computation, Decimals

Problem 5
Percent

Problem 6
Ratio/Proportion

Problem 7
Percent, Money

Problem 8
Integers

Problem 9
Geometry, Surface Area, Money, Percent

Problem 10
Computation, Percent

Tile Job

Teaching Goal

After participating in this lesson, students should be able to identify the missing piece of information that is preventing them from solving the problem. They should also be able to choose a number or other data that will enable them to solve the problem. They should understand that there is a range of possible numbers or data that could be used to solve the problem.

Problem

> Irena and Pavel are tilesetters who have been hired to tile the counter in a new restaurant. The restaurant owner wants them to use 6-inch-square tiles, which will be installed to cover the surface of the 12-foot-long counter. How many tiles will be needed for the job?

Teaching Plan

1. Write the above information on the overhead projector, chalkboard, or white board.
2. Ask students to read the information.
3. Lead a discussion with the whole class using the following questions as part of the discussion:

   What question is being asked? How many tiles will be needed for the job?

  0-7622-1353-1

What information do you know from the problem?
The surface of a 12-foot-long counter must be covered with 6-inch-square tiles.

Why can't you answer the question? The width of the counter is not known.

Could you figure out how many tiles would be needed if you knew the width of the counter? Yes.

Pick a reasonable number for the width of the counter.
3 feet

Now, how many 6-inch-square tiles would be needed to cover the counter? 144 tiles (Students find the area of the counter by multiplying: $12 \text{ ft} \times 3 \text{ ft} = 36 \text{ ft}^2$. You may wish to draw this diagram on the board to make it clear that four 6-in. tiles are needed to cover 1 ft^2, so $4 \times 36 = 144$ tiles are needed to cover 36ft^2.)

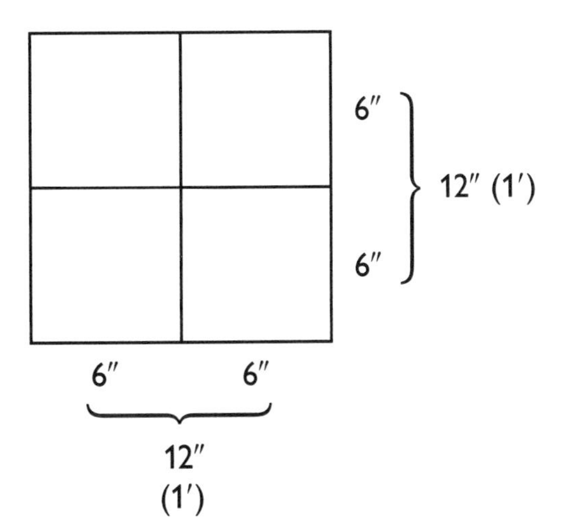

Repeat the above procedure using different numbers for the width of the counter. Students should see that they could solve the problem once they know the width of the counter.

Section 5

Name ....

Problem 1 **Just Four Colors**

A box on the art teacher's desk holds 18 markers. The box contains the same number of blue markers as green. Four of the markers are red and the rest are yellow. If Ian reaches into the box and grabs one marker without looking, what is the probability that he will grab a yellow marker?

1. What is the question? ______________________________

____

____

2. What information do you know from the problem?

____

____

3. What else do you need to know to solve the problem? ______________________________

____

____

____

____

4. Pick a reasonable number for the information you need. ______________________________

5. What is the probability that the marker Ian grabs from the box will be yellow?

____

Name ....

Problem 2 End-of-School Savings

Here are the regular prices of some school supplies at a local store. On the last day of school, everything went on sale for 20% off. That day, Sarah bought 7 notebooks and 5 erasers. The next week, she made a profit on them by selling 4 of the notebooks to kids in her summer-school class. By how much did Sarah's profit lower her cost for the remaining 3 notebooks?

1. What is the question? ______________________________

____

____

2. What information do you know from the problem? ______________________________

____

____

3. What else do you need to know to solve the problem? ______________________________

____

____

4. Pick a reasonable number for the information you need. ______________________________

5. By how much did Sarah's profit lower her cost for the remaining 3 notebooks?

____

Name ....

Problem 3 **Photo Finish**

The photography teacher, Mr. Lifton, developed some students' photographs, which he wants to use for a parents'-night display. He began working at 8:30 a.m. It took him 45 minutes to develop and print each photo and 30 minutes to mount it. How many photos did he develop, print, and mount that day?

1. What is the question? ______________________________

____

____

2. What information do you know from the problem? ______________________________

____

____

3. What else do you need to know to solve the problem? ______________________________

____

____

____

____

4. Pick a reasonable number for the information you need. ______________________________

5. How many photos did he develop, print, and mount that day?

____

Name ....

Problem 4 Gas Up

Just before the Johnsons left for a weekend at the lake, they stopped at the gas station to fill up. They enjoyed their three days of tennis, swimming, fishing, and hiking. They spent $75 a night for two nights at the lodge, $110 for food, and $65 on their activities. As soon as they returned home, Mrs. Johnson pointed out that they had driven 340 miles on 14 gallons of gas. What did it cost the Johnsons for their weekend trip?

1. What is the question? ____________________

____

____

2. What information do you know from the problem? ____________________

____

____

3. What else do you need to know to solve the problem? ____________________

____

____

4. Pick a reasonable number for the information you need. ____________________

5. What did it cost the Johnsons for their weekend trip?

____

Name ....

Problem 5 **Going by the Book**

Two years ago, Raquel bought a brand-new car. Today she checked the book value of her car and learned that in the two years she had owned it, the car's value had depreciated by about 30%. What is her car worth now?

1. What is the question? ____________________

____

____

2. What information do you know from the problem? ____________________

____

____

3. What else do you need to know to solve the problem? ____________________

____

____

____

____

4. Pick a reasonable number for the information you need. ____________________

5. What is the car worth now? ____________________

Name ....

Problem 6 Farm Work

Bill and Charley work on a farm filling bags with 10 pounds of potatoes. Charley can fill 3 bags in the same time it takes Bill to fill 2. They began work one morning at 8:30 a.m. and stopped for lunch at 11:30 a.m. How many bags had they each filled that morning?

1. What is the question? ______________________________

____

____

2. What information do you know from the problem? ______________________________

____

____

____

3. What else do you need to know to solve the problem? ______________________________

____

____

____

____

4. Pick a reasonable number for the information you need. ______________________________

5. How many bags had they each filled that morning? ______________________________

Name ....

Problem 7 **Rain Gear**

Theo charges the same price for each umbrella and poncho he sells at the amusement park. One rainy day, a school group bought 40% of his stock. A senior-citizen club bought 25% of what was left, and a busload of tourists bought the rest. How much did each group pay Theo?

1. What is the question? ______________________________

____

____

2. What information do you know from the problem? ______________________________

____

____

3. What else do you need to know to solve the problem? ______________________________

____

____

____

____

4. Pick a reasonable number for the information you need. ______________________________

5. How much did each group pay Theo? ______________________________

Name ....

Problem 8 **Kickoff!**

In Sunday's football game, the Panthers returned the opening kickoff 23 yards. On the first play, they gained 18 yards. On the second play, they lost 9 yards. On the third play, they gained 2 yards. This brought them to what yard marker on the football field?

1. What is the question? ______________________________

____

____

2. What information do you know from the problem? ______________________________

____

____

3. What else do you need to know to solve the problem? ______________________________

____

____

____

____

4. Pick a reasonable number for the information you need. ______________________________

5. This brought them to what yard marker on the football field?

____

Name ....

Problem 9 **Paint Job**

Mrs. Harris hired a college student to paint the outside of the storage shed shown in the diagram. Everything needs to be painted, except the two slanted parts of the roof, which are covered with shingles. One gallon of the paint that Mrs. Harris wants to buy covers 400 square feet and costs $24.95. How much will she pay for the paint she needs including 6% sales tax?

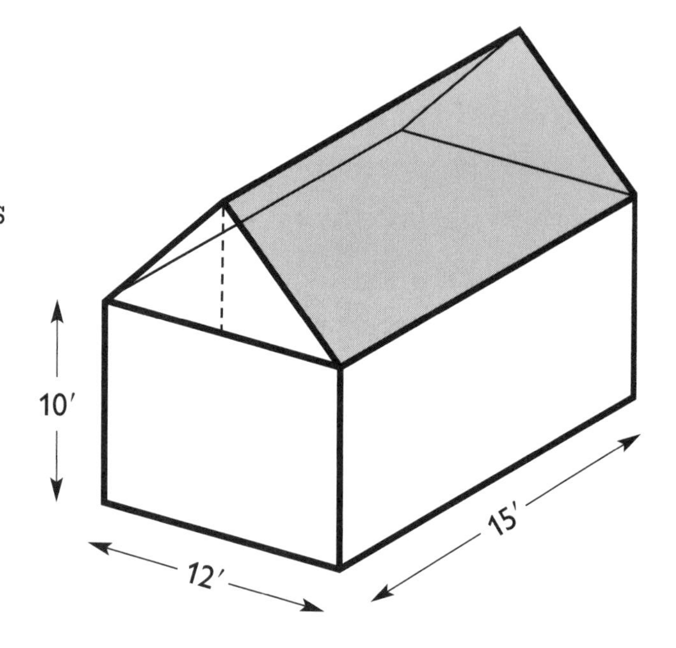

1. What is the question? ______________________________

____

____

2. What information do you know from the problem? ______________________________

____

____

3. What else do you need to know to solve the problem? ______________________________

____

____

4. Pick a reasonable number for the information you need. ______________________________

5. How much will she pay for the paint she needs including 6% sales tax?

____

Name ....

Problem 10 Cake Sale

On Tuesday, the owners of the Main Street Cakery sold 50% of the cakes they baked to restaurants, 300 of the cakes to stores, and 180 of the cakes to a supermarket chain. They donated the remaining cakes to a homeless shelter. How many cakes were baked at the Cakery on Tuesday?

1. What is the question? ______________________

____

____

2. What information do you know from the problem? ______________________

____

____

3. What else do you need to know to solve the problem? ______________________

____

____

____

____

4. Pick a reasonable number for the information you need. ______________________

5. How many cakes were baked at the Cakery on Tuesday? ______________________

Answer Key

Answers 4–6 will vary with each problem depending on the data that the student supplies.

Problem 1: Just Four Colors

1. What is the probability that Ian will grab a yellow marker?
2. There are equal numbers of blue and green markers, four red markers, and some number of yellow for a total of 18 markers.
3. You need to know the number of blue and green markers.

Problem 2: End-of-School Savings

1. By how much did Sarah's profit lower her cost for the remaining 3 notebooks?
2. Sarah bought 7 notebooks at 20% off the original price of $2.00 each.
3. You need to know the price at which Sarah sold each notebook.

Problem 3: Photo Finish

1. How many photos did he develop, print, and mount that day?
2. Mr. Lifton began working at 8:30 a.m. It took him 45 minutes to develop and print each photo and 30 minutes to mount it.
3. You need to know the time at which he stopped working for the day.

Problem 4: Gas Up

1. What did it cost the Johnsons for their weekend trip?
2. They spent $75 a night for two nights at the lodge, $110 for food, and $65 on their activities. They used 14 gallons of gasoline.
3. You need to know the price per gallon that they paid for gasoline.

Problem 5: Going by the Book

1. What is the car worth now?
2. The car is now worth 70% of its original price.
3. You need to know the original price of the car.

Problem 6: Farm Work

1. How many bags did Charley and Bill each fill that morning?
2. In three hours, Bill filled $\frac{2}{3}$ of the number of bags that Charley filled.
3. You need to know how many bags one of the boys filled that morning.

Problem 7: Rain Gear

1. How much did each group pay Theo?
2. A school group bought 40% of his stock, senior citizens bought 25% of what was left, and tourists bought the rest.
3. You need to know how much money Theo took in that day.

Problem 8: Kickoff!

1. This brought them to what yard marker on the football field?
2. The Panthers returned the opening kickoff 23 yards. Then they gained 18 yards, lost 9 yards, and gained 2 yards.
3. You need to know where they were on the field when they received the opening kickoff.

Problem 9: Paint Job

1. How much will she pay for the paint she needs including 6% sales tax?
2. The entire shed needs to be painted, except the two slanted parts of the roof. One gallon of paint covers 400 square feet and costs $24.95.
3. You need to know the height of the triangular sides of the roof.

Problem 10: Cake Sale

1. How many cakes were baked on Tuesday?
2. They sold 50% of their cakes to restaurants, 300 cakes to stores, and 180 cakes to a supermarket chain. They donated the rest of their cakes to a shelter.
3. You need to know how many cakes they gave to the shelter.

Assessment Note

Student work on any of the problems in this section can be assessed using the 3-point rubric on page ix.

Section 6 What's the Question if You Know the Answer?

THE MATHEMATICAL SITUATIONS in Section 6 do not include questions. This section encourages reasoning and the ability to work backward from a specific answer. Students are asked to generate their own questions based on specific answers.

It is recommended that the teaching problem that follows be used as a whole-class activity.

The procedures outlined in the teaching problem will help students learn how to construct a question for a specific answer.

Working in small groups or in pairs is suggested as students learn to identify the correct question or to construct questions. This will allow them to discuss their thinking with one another. Once students are comfortable with the process, they can work independently.

Whole-group discussion is especially important in this section, even after students are working independently. A question based on specific information can be framed in various ways. Discussing what makes a good question and seeing well-constructed questions modeled will help students become more proficient at writing their own good questions. Students should also talk about how they arrive at a given answer. Knowing how to obtain the answer is crucial when constructing the question. It is important for the teacher as well as students to hear the thinking verbalized.

Mathematical Skills

Teaching Problem
Algebra, Fractions

Problem 1
Data Analysis, Venn Diagram

Problem 2
Probability

Problem 3
Percent, Money

Problem 4
Geometry, Pythagorean Theorem

Problem 5
Computation, Money

Problem 6
Percent, Money, Discount

Problem 7
Fractions

Problem 8
Geometry, Measurement

Problem 9
Patterns, Square Numbers

Problem 10
Percent, Money

Keeping Score

Teaching Goal

After participating in this lesson, students should be able to generate a variety of questions based on the given data. They should be able to construct a question for a specific answer.

Problem

> After the first quarter of last week's football game, the Dolphins were scoreless. In the second quarter, they scored half of their total number of points. In the third quarter, they scored one third of their total points. In the final quarter, they scored 6 points.

Teaching Plan

1. Write the above information on the overhead projector, chalkboard, or white board.
2. Ask students to read the information.
3. Have students hone in on finding the correct question for a given answer. Give a specific answer based on the numerical data and ask students to find a question for that answer.

   What's the question if the answer is 36? What was the Dolphins' total score?

   What's the question if the answer is 18? How many points did the Dolphins score in the second quarter?

   What's the question if the answer is 12? How many points did the Dolphins score in the third quarter?

   What's the question if the answer is 0 points? How many points did the Dolphins score in the first quarter?

4. Make sure that students understand that the answers can be found in more than one way. For example, using algebra:

Let x = total number of points scored

$\frac{x}{2}$ = number of points scored in second quarter

$\frac{x}{3}$ = number of points scored in third quarter

Therefore,

$x = \frac{x}{2} + \frac{x}{3} + 6$

So, if $x = 36$, then $\frac{x}{2} = 18$ and $\frac{x}{3} = 12$.

Alternatively, students could work backwards starting with the 6 points that the Dolphins scored in the last quarter: $\frac{1}{2} + \frac{1}{3} = \frac{5}{6}$; Then, $\frac{1}{6} = 6$, $\frac{6}{6} = 36$, $\frac{1}{2} = 18$, and $\frac{1}{3} = 12$.

5. To help students having difficulty perceiving the solutions, draw a rectangle on the board and divide it into four equal sections. Mark the sections "1st quarter," "2nd quarter," "3rd quarter," and "4th quarter." Then write 0, $\frac{x}{2}$, $\frac{x}{3}$, and 6 in the corresponding sections.

This is an excellent reasoning exercise. Initially, some students may have difficulty constructing questions that can be answered by a given number. If you find that your students are having difficulty with this lesson, you may wish to try an additional lesson or two with the whole class before asking students to continue working the next problems with a small group or in pairs.

Name ....

Problem 1 **Three Attractions**

The Outdoor Club went to an amusement park for the day. The Venn diagram shows how many of the club members enjoyed three of the park's attractions.

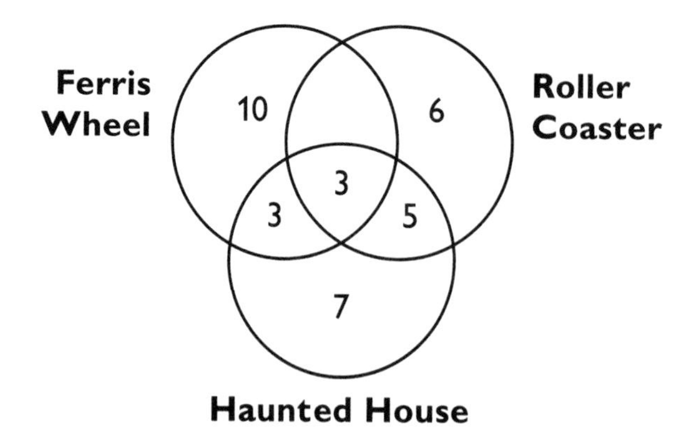

1. What's the question if the answer is 16? ______________________________

____

____

2. What's the question if the answer is 14? ______________________________

____

____

3. What's the question if the answer is 18? ______________________________

____

____

4. What's the question if the answer is 3? ______________________________

____

____

5. What's the question if the answer is 5? ______________________________

____

____

Name ....

Problem 2 **Soup Cans**

Suzie's little sister, Yolanda, tore the labels off 10 cans of soup. Now the cans all look exactly alike so Suzie can't tell them apart. She knows that 3 of the cans contain tomato soup, 2 contain clam chowder, 4 contain minestrone soup, and 1 contains pea soup. Suzie picks one of the cans at random and opens it.

1. What's the question if the answer is $\frac{3}{10}$? ______________________________

____

____

2. What's the question if the answer is $\frac{4}{10}$? ______________________________

____

____

3. What's the question if the answer is $\frac{9}{10}$? ______________________________

____

____

4. What's the question if the answer is $\frac{5}{10}$? ______________________________

____

____

5. What's the question if the answer is 0? ______________________________

____

Name ....

Problem 3 **Money for Recycling**

Mark collects aluminum cans and bottles and sells them to the recycling center. The center pays $.05 for each can and 40% more for each bottle. Last Sunday, Mark took 140 cans and 48 bottles to the center.

1. What's the question if the answer is $.07? ______

2. What's the question if the answer is $7.00? ______

3. What's the question if the answer is $3.36? ______

4. What's the question if the answer is $10.36? ______

Name ....

Problem 4 Rectangle and Triangles

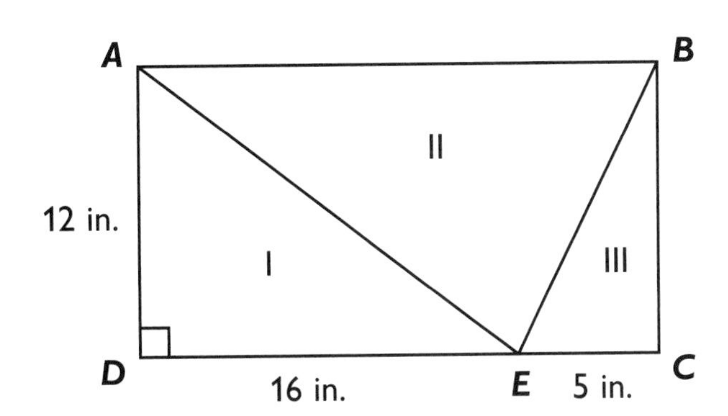

1. What's the question if the answer is 96 square inches?

____

____

2. What's the question if the answer is 30 square inches?

____

____

3. What's the question if the answer is 126 square inches?

____

____

4. What's the question if the answer is 20 inches?

____

____

5. What's the question if the answer is 252 square inches?

____

____

Name ....

Problem 5 **Wonderland Weekend**

At Wonderland, a 1-day pass costs $20. A 3-day pass costs $47. The on-site Wonderland Hotel charges $125 per room for each night, including breakfast and dinner. An off-site motel charges $45 a night without meals. Four friends are going to spend 3 days at Wonderland. They plan to share a room for 2 nights.

1. What's the question if the answer is $47? ______________________________

____

2. What's the question if the answer is $188? ______________________________

____

____

3. What's the question if the answer is $250? ______________________________

____

____

4. What's the question if the answer is $438? ______________________________

____

____

5. What's the question if the answer is $80? ______________________________

____

____

Name ....

Problem 6 New Sofa

Joyce is shopping for a living-room sofa. The tag on the sofa she likes is marked $890, but today the store is having a 35%-off sale on all sofas. The salesperson tells Joyce that if she pays for the sofa in cash today, she will get an additional 10% discount off the sale price.

1. What's the question if the answer is $890? ______________________________

____

____

2. What's the question if the answer is $578.50? ______________________________

____

____

3. What's the question if the answer is $520.65? ______________________________

____

____

4. What's the question if the answer is $311.50? ______________________________

____

____

Name ....

Problem 7 Museum Visit

Thirty-three seventh-graders went on a trip to the science museum. As soon as they got there, one third of the entire group headed for the computer exhibit. Six others from the group went to the Sound-and-Light-Atorium. One fourth of those who were left ran toward the Space Show. The remaining students lined up for the Sci-Max film.

1. What's the question if the answer is 33?

____

____

2. What's the question if the answer is 6?

____

____

3. What's the question if the answer is 11?

____

____

4. What's the question if the answer is 4?

____

____

5. What's the question if the answer is 12?

____

Name ....

Problem 8 **Anti-Static Paint**

The walls and ceiling of the computer room are about to be painted with anti-static paint. The painter needs to buy enough paint to cover the walls and ceiling of this windowless, rectangular room, which measures 30 feet by 15 feet by 8 feet.

1. What's the question if the answer is 120 square feet? ______________________

____

____

____

2. What's the question if the answer is 240 square feet? ______________________

____

____

____

3. What's the question if the answer is 450 square feet? ______________________

____

____

4. What's the question if the answer is 1,170 square feet? ______________________

____

____

____

Name ....

Problem 9 **Triangular Pattern**

Study the pattern shown below:

Row 1	**1**
Row 2	**1 + 3**
Row 3	**1 + 3 + 5**
Row 4	**1 + 3 + 5 + 7**
Row 5	**1 + 3 + 5 + 7 + 9**
:	
:	

1. What's the question if the answer is 9? ________________________________

____

____

2. What's the question if the answer is 5? ________________________________

____

____

3. What's the question if the answer is 25? ________________________________

____

____

4. What's the question if the answer is 8? ________________________________

____

5. What's the question if the answer is a perfect square? ____________________

____

Name ....

Problem 10 **Rose Bouquets**

A florist ordered 15 dozen roses at $18 per dozen. When her order arrived, she saw that 10% of the roses were withered and she threw them away. She sold the remaining roses in bouquets of 9 for $20.

1. What's the question if the answer is $270?

2. What's the question if the answer is 18?

3. What's the question if the answer is $360?

4. What's the question if the answer is $90?

Answer Key

Problem 1: Three Attractions

1. How many club members went on the Ferris wheel?
2. How many club members went on the roller coaster?
3. How many club members went into the haunted house?
4. How many club members enjoyed all three activities? *OR:* How many went on the Ferris wheel and into the haunted house but not on the roller coaster?
5. How many club members went on the roller coaster and into the haunted house?

Problem 2: Soup Cans

1. What is the probability that the can contains tomato soup?
2. What is the probability that the can contains minestrone soup?
3. What is the probability that the can does not contain pea soup?
4. What is the probability that the can contains either clam chowder or tomato soup?
5. What is the probability that the can contains chicken soup? *(Or, any other kind of soup not mentioned in the problem)*

Problem 3: Money for Recycling

1. How much money did Mark receive for each bottle?
2. How much money did Mark receive for the cans?
3. How much money did Mark receive for all the bottles?
4. How much money did Mark receive for all the cans and 2 bottles?

Problem 4: Rectangle and Triangles

1. What is the area of $\triangle ADE$?
2. What is the area of $\triangle BCE$?
3. What is the area of $\triangle ABE$?
4. What is the length of line segment AE?
5. What is the area of rectangle $ABCD$?

Problem 5: Wonderland Weekend

1. How much does one 3-day pass cost?
2. How much will all four friends pay for their 3-day passes?
3. How much would 2 nights at the Wonderland Hotel cost?
4. How much would 3-day passes and 2 nights at the Wonderland Hotel cost?
5. How much more per night does a room cost at the Wonderland Hotel than at the off-site motel?

Problem 6: New Sofa

1. What was the regular price of the sofa before the sale?
2. What is the sale price of the sofa?
3. How much will the sofa cost if Joyce buys it today and pays with cash?
4. What will be the amount of discount if Joyce buys the sofa but does not pay with cash?

Problem 7: Museum Visit

1. How many seventh-graders went to the science museum?
2. How many went to the Sound-and-Light-Atorium?
3. How many seventh-graders went to the computer exhibit?
4. How many seventh-graders went to the Space Show?
5. How many seventh-graders went to see the Sci-Max film?

Problem 8: Anti-Static Paint

1. How much paint will be needed to cover one of the 8-by-15-ft walls?
2. How much paint will be needed to cover the two 8-by-15-ft walls?
3. How much paint will be needed to cover the ceiling?
4. How much paint will be needed to complete the whole job?

Problem 9: Triangular Pattern

1. What is the sum of the terms in Row 3?
2. How many terms are in Row 5?
3. What is the sum of the terms in Row 5? *OR:* What is the square of the number of terms in Row 5?
4. How many terms would there be in Row 8?
5. What could you call the sum of the terms in each row?

Problem 10: Rose Bouquets

1. How much did the florist pay for her order?
2. How many roses did the florist throw away? *OR:* How many bouquets did she sell?
3. How much money did she get for all the bouquets she sold?
4. What was the florist's profit?

Assessment Note

Student work on any of the problems in this section can be assessed using the 3-point rubric on page ix.